THE COMPLETE ORGAN MARCHES

Wise Publications
London/New York/Sydney

Exclusive distributors:
Music Sales Limited
8/9 Frith Street, London W1V 5TZ, England
Music Sales Pty. Limited,
120 Rothschild Avenue, Rosebery, NSW 2018, Australia.

This book © Copyright 1987 by
Wise Publications
ISBN 0.7119.1129.0
Order No. AM 65822

Designed by Kate Hepburn & Pearce Marchbank.

Music Sales' complete catalogue lists thousands of
titles and is free from your local music shop,
or direct from Music Sales Limited.
Please send a cheque or Postal Order for £1.50 for postage
to Music Sales Limited, 8/9 Frith Street, London, W1V 5TZ.

Printed in Great Britain by
J. B. Offset Printers (Marks Tey) Limited

MARCHES

SONS OF THE BRAVE

By: Thomas Bidgood

Upper: clarinet + flutes 16′ 8′ 4′ (80 8064 000), with tremolo
Lower: flutes (with tremolo) + strings
Pedal: 16′ + 8′
Drums: march ♩♩, or ♩♩ ♩ = 92

STARS AND STRIPES

By: J. P. Sousa

Upper: brass ensemble
Lower: flutes (with tremolo) + strings
Pedal: 16' + 8'
Drums: march 4/4, or 2/4 ♩ = 92

Upper: brass to clarinet
and flutes

MARCHE MILITAIRE

By: Franz Schubert

Upper: string ensemble
Lower: flutes (with tremolo)
Pedal: 16' + 8'
Drums: march $\frac{4}{4}$, or $\frac{2}{4}$ $\; \d = 88$

D.%. al Coda

Upper: cut clarinet

CODA

12

AMERICAN PATROL

By: F. W. Meacham

Upper: trumpet solo
Lower: flutes (with tremolo)
Pedal: 16' + 8'
Drums: march ($\frac{4}{4}$ or $\frac{2}{4}$) $\quad \textbf{.} = 92$

14

D.℘. al Coda
Upper: cut flutes

CODA

15

RADETZKY MARCH

By: Johann Strauss Sr.

Upper: brass ensemble + vibraphone
Lower: flute 8′, string 8′
Pedal: 16′ + 8′
Drums: march 4/4 or 2/4 ♩ = 100

FUNERAL MARCH OF A MARIONETTE

By: Charles Gounod

Upper: bassoon (or horn)
Lower: flutes (with tremolo)
Pedal: 16' + 8'
Drums: march $\frac{6}{8}$ ♩.= 92

ENTRY OF THE GLADIATORS

By: J. Fucik

Upper: brass ensemble
Lower: flutes (with tremolo) + strings
Pedal: 16′ + 8′
Drums: march $\frac{4}{4}$, or $\frac{2}{4}$ ♩ = 92

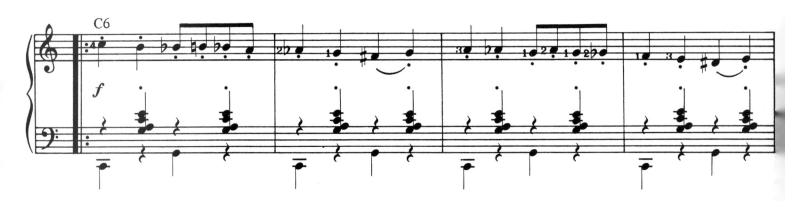

LIBERTY BELL

By: J. P. Sousa

Upper: brass ensemble
Lower: flutes (with tremolo) + strings
Pedal: 16' + 8'
Drums: march 6/8 ♩.= 88

RAKOCZY MARCH

By: Franz Liszt

Upper: piano
Lower: flutes (with tremolo)
Pedal: 16' + 8'
Drums: march 4/4 or 2/4 ♩ = 80

* E7, omitting note D   ** Dm7, omitting note C

WASHINGTON POST

By: J. P. Sousa

Upper: brass ensemble
Lower: flutes (with tremolo) + strings
Pedal: 16' + 8'
Drums: march $\frac{6}{8}$ ♩. = 112

MARCH FROM "CARMEN"

By: Georges Bizet

Upper: string ensemble + trumpet
Lower: flutes (with tremolo) + strings
Pedal: 16' + 8'
Drums: march $\frac{4}{4}$ or $\frac{2}{4}$ ♩ = 104

MARCH OF THE TOYS (from "The Nutcracker")

By: Peter Tchaikovsky

Upper: brass ensemble
Lower: flutes (with tremolo)
Pedal: 16' + 8'
Drums: march 2/4 or 4/4 ♩ = 100

UNDER THE DOUBLE EAGLE

By: J. F. Wagner

Upper: flute + clarinet (with vibrato)
Lower: flutes (with tremolo) + strings
Pedal: 16' + 8'
Drums: march $\frac{2}{4}$ ♩ = 100

Upper: add strings

POMP AND CIRCUMSTANCE MARCH, No. 1

By: Edward Elgar

Upper: string ensemble
Lower: flutes (with tremolo) + strings
Pedal: 16′ + 8′
Drums: march 4/4, or 2/4 ♩ = 88

43

CHORD CHARTS (For Left Hand)

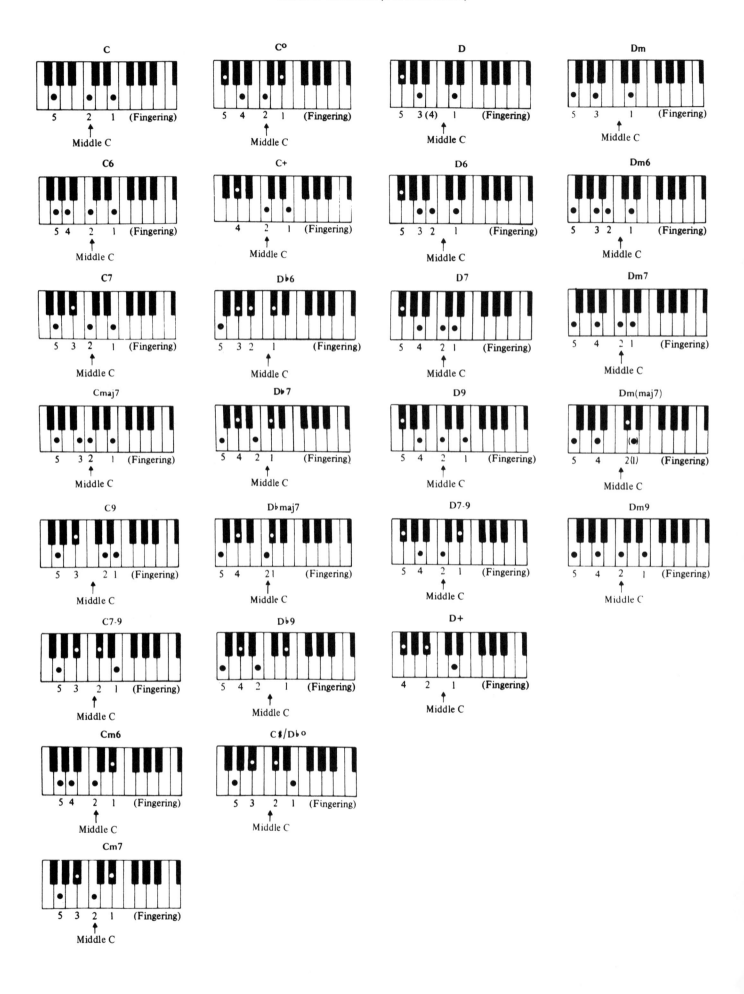

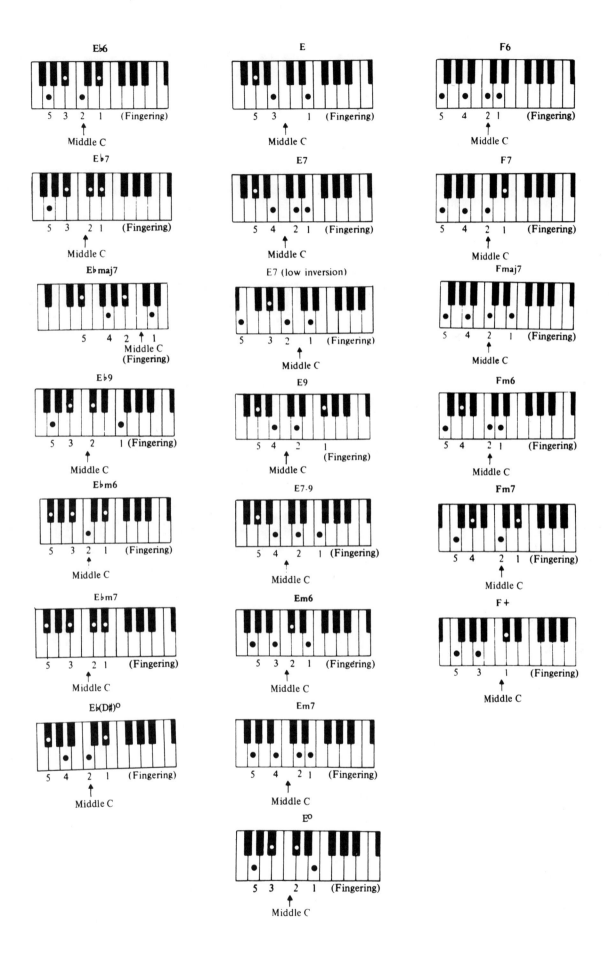

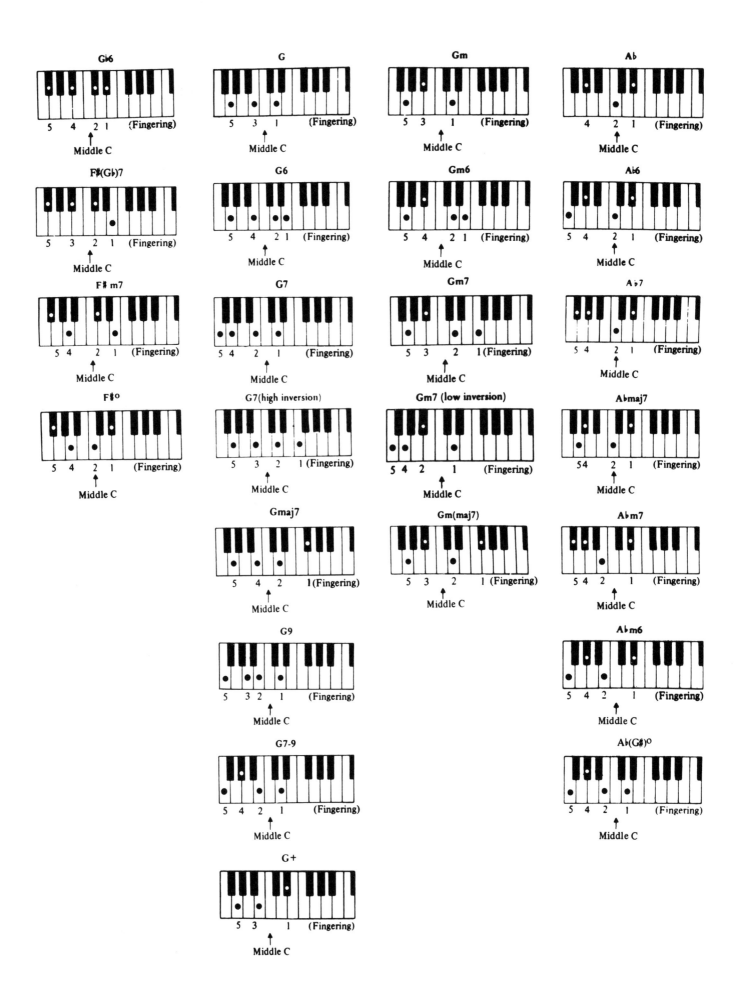

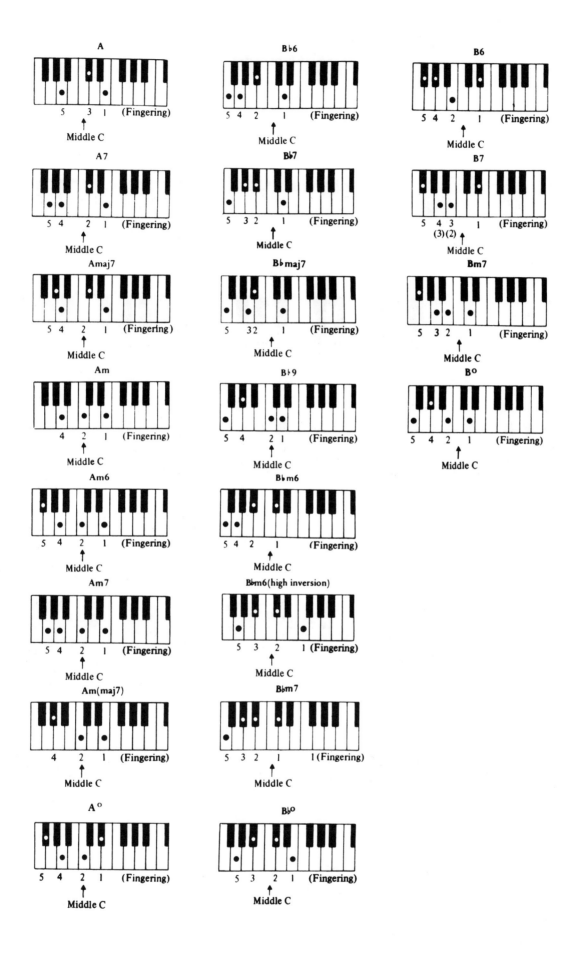

KEYBOARD/PEDAL - BOARD CHART

THE NOTES OF BOTH KEYBOARDS (MANUALS) AND PEDAL-BOARD

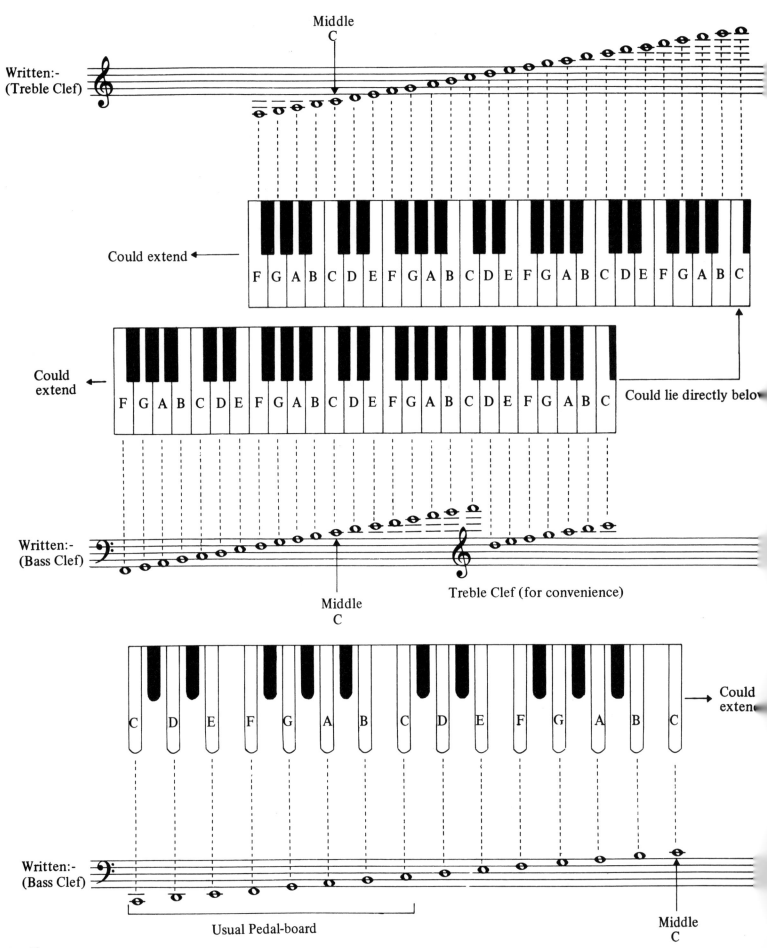